THE WORLD OF
VERONICA ROTH'S
DIVERGENT
SERIES

KATHERINE TEGEN BOOKS
An Imprint of HarperCollins Publishers

Katherine Tegen Books is an imprint of HarperCollins Publishers.

The World of Veronica Roth's Divergent Series
Copyright © 2011, 2012 by Veronica Roth

ISBN 978-0-06-223491-9

Typography by Joel Tippie
12 13 14 15 16   CG/BR   10 9 8 7 6 5 4 3 2 1
❖
First Edition

CONTENTS

Q&A with Veronica Roth

Why do you feel people are naturally drawn to reading books about dystopian societies?

There are many reasons, I'm sure, but I think dystopian books are perfect for people who like to ask "what if?" but want to see their "what if?" questions played out in a world that has the same rules as our own (as opposed to paranormal or fantasy, in which the rules of the world—in terms of physics, or biology, or something—are a little different). There is also something extremely interesting about looking at the world now, reading about a possible future world, and imagining the steps in between. It's imaginative, yet grounded in the real world. I also love that the majority of the characters in dystopian and post-apocalyptic literature have a lot of agency—they take charge of their lives in environments that make it hard for them to do so, and I love reading about strong characters like that.

Where did the idea of DIVERGENT come from?

At the time that I came up with the idea for DIVERGENT (about six years ago), I was studying exposure therapy in the treatment of phobias. Exposure therapy involves confronting a person with the stimulus that scares them (heights, spiders, etc.) repeatedly, in a safe environment, until their brain rewires and they aren't afraid of it anymore. This is where the Dauntless initiation process comes from—I wanted to write about a subculture of people who want to eradicate fear, and exposure therapy is how they go about doing it. I was also beginning to learn about social psychology and the Milgram experiment on obedience to authority figures, which made me think about how malleable our supposedly strict moral codes become in the right conditions. Something that DIVERGENT grapples with.

But really, what got me to write it down was that I was driving somewhere and listening to a song and I just imagined someone jumping off a building, but not for a self-destructive reason. And I wondered why someone would do that, and the exposure therapy thing was the answer. And thus, Dauntless was born.

How and why did you start writing? And what inspires you?

I studied Creative Writing in college because it was the only thing I loved enough to do all the time. But I started writing because I decided I was too old to play pretend in the backyard. Then I found that I could create those imaginary worlds on the page. I think I was in fifth grade or sixth grade when I started.

What inspires me now . . . well, that's a hard question! I try to follow my curiosity. I did that with DIVERGENT—I was curious about phobias and how to treat them, and learning about that helped me come up with the Dauntless initiation process. These days I'm curious about the northern lights and the social organization of ants. I have no idea how those things could make a book, but I don't worry about it—I just learn about what interests me, and write about what I find my mind returning to, and see what happens.

Is there a character in DIVERGENT who you like especially? If so, why?

I love a lot of the characters, but one of my favorites is Tobias. To me he seems to have a rich off-screen life. I can imagine what he's doing at any given moment, even if he's not with Tris. I try to do that with all the characters, but for him, it has always come naturally. I also think he balances strength with vulnerability well.

What made you choose Chicago as the setting for your book?

It wasn't a conscious decision, at first. I set the book in a city that felt familiar to me. What clued me in to the fact that it was Chicago was the trains—constantly running, all over the city, like the El in present-day Chicago. I wrote about the Dauntless riding the trains before I realized that the only place I have ever been where trains are aboveground and in constant motion is Chicago—that I had been writing about my favorite city without even knowing it. I have lived next to Chicago since I was five years old, so it is both familiar to me and unfamiliar, because I've never actually lived there. As I worked more and more of the city into the manuscript, I got the chance to rediscover my home, which was wonderful—there's so much I don't know about it! But my personal connections with the place aside, I also found it interesting to turn such a clean and organized place upside down.

If you had to choose, which faction would you join?
I've decided there's a difference between figuring out which faction you have aptitude for and choosing which one you'd like to be in. No one fits into a faction perfectly, so determining your aptitude is extremely difficult. But as for choosing a faction, it's all about priorities. Do you value happiness over justice? You might be Amity. How about honesty over kindness? Candor. And I would choose Dauntless, probably, because I believe in freedom and justice over comfort and safety. I might die during

initiation. I'm almost sure of it, actually. I believe I would choose Dauntless not because of a thirst for freedom, although that's certainly appealing, but because I think courage is so important. I would be compelled to choose them not by aptitude, necessarily, but by ideology. For the record, though, my favorite faction is Abnegation, so I might pick them if I was too afraid to choose Dauntless. I think the way they live is fascinating, and they, though not without their flaws, generally live beautiful, good lives.

This book is full of heart-pounding action, which begs the question, are you a thrill-seeker at heart?
Absolutely not. I am terrified of heights. And speed. And danger of any kind. Sometimes writing DIVERGENT gave me vertigo. Like in the zip line scene—even if you paid me a billion dollars, I would never do what Tris does in that scene. I don't think I'm a coward, but I don't like to take unnecessary risks. Also, I'm a writer, and as a group, we tend to be built for coffee shops, carpal tunnel syndrome, and comfortable chairs rather than jumping off buildings.

What characteristics did you keep in mind when you were coming up with the main character, Beatrice?
I don't think I ever sat down and thought about how

Beatrice was—I just had this sense of her, like I *knew* her. I did set myself a rule that was hard to follow, though: Beatrice is always the agent. That is, she's always choosing, always acting, always moving the plot by her behavior. I don't know that I succeeded in keeping that rule, but it was helpful for me when trying to create an active, rather than a passive or reactive, character.

How has your childhood influenced your writing?
My mother read to me every night when I was young, so that's probably where my love of books began. And also, if I ever complained about being bored, my mother said, "Boredom is not allowed," so I guess you could say that the rules of our house demanded that I be creative. It worked, though, because I used to go outside every day and invent these elaborate worlds and scenarios in my head, and when I grew too old for playing pretend, I started to write everything down instead. Nicely done, Mom.

What book(s) changed your life and why?
I could probably list books for days, so I'll just list a few favorites: *The Giver* by Lois Lowry, *Ender's Game* by Orson Scott Card, *A Wrinkle in Time* by Madeleine L'Engle, the Animorphs series by K.A. Applegate, *1984* by George Orwell, the Bible, *Gilead* by Marilynne Robinson, and

Juliet by Andras Visky (which is a play, but I think it still counts). Some have taught me about writing, but even if they didn't, they all inspired me, challenged me, encouraged me, and guided me in different ways. I don't think books have ever solved my problems or made my decisions for me, but they bring me out of myself and make me ask myself questions, and that's life altering enough.

Do you think that you make wise or flawed decisions? Why?

I make both. Doesn't everyone? Usually the flawed ones are decisions I think are wise but are really motivated by something else—pride, maybe, or selfishness—and the wise ones happen when I'm not paying attention, or at those brief moments I succeed at loving the people around me. To be honest, the flawed ones are probably more common. But I try to learn from them.

How do you get through a dark day?

For me, one of the worst things I can do on a bad day is withdraw from people—but it's one of the easiest things for me to do. In the past few years I've been learning to rely on friends and family. Now, when my pride says "Deal with it yourself," I try to say, "Screw that. I need help." I have realized that there's no shame in letting the people I love take care of me. Most of the time they do a better job at it than I even realize.

What thought or message would you put in a fortune cookie?
"Stop reading this. Eat the cookie and live your life."

Quotations that Inspired divergent

VERONICA: This quote was actually integral to my discovery of Tris's voice. I wanted to create a character who could and would deliver that line, and Tris can and will. Her voice is clipped, direct, and strong, just like these lines.

> *"My will is mine. . . I shall not make it soft for you."*
> —Agamemnon, *Aeschylus*

VERONICA: Sometimes I imagine Tris repeating this to herself during her initiation, over and over again.

> *"I must not fear. Fear is the mind-killer. Fear is the little-death that brings total obliteration. I will face my fear. I will permit it to pass over me and through me. And when it has gone past I will turn the inner eye to see its path. Where the fear has gone there will be nothing. Only I will remain."*
> —Dune *by Frank Herbert*

VERONICA: This, I imagine, is what Tris's enemies would say to her. And they would be wrong.

> *"Well, let her know the stubbornest of wills*
> *Are soonest bended, as the hardest iron,*

O'er-heated in the fire to brittleness,
Flies soonest into fragments, shivered through."
—Antigone, *Sophocles*

VERONICA: A word of advice to the faction that causes so much trouble—and to every flawed human being.

"But if you bite and devour one another, watch out that you are not consumed by one another."
—Galatians 5:15

VERONICA: These lines, I imagine, would inspire the people in Tris's world to fight the good fight.

"Hold on to the world we all remember fighting for
There's some strength left in us yet
Hold on to the world we all remember dying for
There's some hope left in it yet
Arise and be
All that you dreamed."
—"Arise" by Flyleaf

VERONICA: For Tris and the people who help her at the end.

Tho' much is taken, much abides; and tho'
We are not now that strength which in the old days
Moved earth and heaven; that which we are, we are;
One equal temper of heroic hearts,
Made weak by time and fate, but strong in will
To strive, to seek, to find, and not to yield.
—"Ulysses," Lord Alfred Tennyson

Veronica Roth's divergent Playlist

1. "Starts With One" by Shiny Toy Guns. This song gets me in touch with the good aspects of Beatrice's chosen faction.

2. "Chasm" by Flyleaf. And this song gets me in touch with the *bad* aspects of Beatrice's chosen faction.

3. "Come Alive" by Foo Fighters. This is the love interest's song for Beatrice.

4. "Again" by Flyleaf. And this is Beatrice's song for her love interest.

5. "Help I'm Alive" by Metric. This is Beatrice's initiation song.

6. "We Die Young" by The Showdown. This might as well be the theme song for Beatrice's chosen faction— it's what they would choose for themselves.

7. "Canvas" by Imogen Heap. This is the "riding on trains" song.

8. "Running Up That Hill" by Placebo. The tone of this song matches the tone of much of the book, for me.

9. "Sweet Sacrifice" by Evanescence. I was listening to this song when the first scene I wrote (in chapter 6) popped into my head. That scene led me to the world of the book and its basic plot.

10. "Arise" by Flyleaf. A powerful song that's perfect for chapters 38 and 39.

Veronica Roth's insurgent Playlist

I always listen to music while I write, and the music selection process can be tricky, because if I can't find the right song, sometimes it's hard for me to work, which is not ideal! I don't pay attention to genre at all—only to what kind of scene it makes me see.

Here are a few of the songs I listened to while writing and revising INSURGENT:

1. "Timshel" by Mumford & Sons. I don't think anyone could describe Tris as "innocent" after the things she's done and seen, but I do think of her as a person of substance, so these lyrics struck me.

2. "Giants" by Now, Now. There isn't really a specific part of this song that applies to the book, but I listened to it during quite a few action sequences while writing the book, so the general feeling is right.

3. "Hysteria" by Muse. I believe this qualifies as a Dauntless-on-the-verge-of-war song.

4. "The Catalyst" by Linkin Park. This one sort of surprised me—I heard it randomly one day and just stopped in the middle of what I was doing because

it captured the situation of INSURGENT so perfectly—a group of people who Tris calls "creatures of loss," facing an enemy it doesn't feel strong enough to defeat.

5. "Under the Waves" by Pendulum. There are a lot of moments in INSURGENT in which Tris feels overwhelmed. This song is good for that sort of thing.

Veronica Roth
Talks about Utopian Worlds

If utopian fiction became the new trend, instead of dystopian fiction, I wouldn't read it.

If you actually succeed in creating a utopia, you've created a world without conflict, in which everything is perfect. And if there's no conflict, there are no stories worth telling—or reading! It would be all "Jenny thought she might not be able to attain her lifelong dream of marshmallow taste tester for a little while . . . but she did!" and "John's dad said he couldn't go to the movies, so John asked really nicely and his dad changed his mind." I'm bored already.

But if I were going to create a utopia, I would make a world in which people are focused on their personal, moral obligations, and strive to be the best possible version of themselves. They would be allowed to choose whatever path they wanted in life. They would know what was expected of them, they would have a clear purpose, and they would have a strong sense of group identity and belonging. And there would be five factions. . . .

Oh, wait. I tried that already.

But seriously: DIVERGENT was my utopian world. I mean, that wasn't the plan. I never even set out to write *dystopian* fiction, that's just what I had when I was finished—at the beginning, I was just writing about a place I found interesting, and a character with a compelling story, and as I began to build the world, I realized that it was my utopia. And then I realized that my utopia was a terrible place, and no one should ever put me in charge of creating a perfect society.

Maybe it's a little depressing to think that my vision of a perfect world is actually so messed up, but I think it means that I don't really understand what "perfect" is. To me it's all about virtue and responsibility; to someone else it would be about happiness and peace, and happy drugs would be pumped into the water supply—but that sounds like a nightmare, doesn't it? Because both of us are wrong about perfect. We have no idea what it would look like, and our approximations of it are incomplete.

And that gives me a lot of hope, because if I don't know what perfect means, it's not something I can reach on my own. Which means that I can stop trying to be perfect and just try to love the people around me and the things I'm doing. And strangely enough, that's Tris's journey. She tries selflessness on for size, and then she tries bravery, but at the end, it's what she does out of love that's more important than any virtue.

I think maybe utopian fiction would actually look just

like dystopian fiction, depending on who you are. To the heartbroken person, a world that eradicates love might be a utopia; to the rest of us, it isn't. To the person who doesn't have a plan, a world in which everything is planned out for you might be a utopia; to those of us who like to choose our own adventure, it's definitely not.

So maybe I've changed my mind—maybe I would read utopian fiction. Or *maybe I already am*. What a scary thought.

FACTION NAMING WITH VERONICA ROTH

I have been asked in the past if I made up the words for the faction names. I didn't, but I did intentionally choose unfamiliar words, for an assortment of reasons. One of them is that I wanted to slow down comprehension of what each faction stands for, so you learn as much by observing as by the name of the faction itself. Another is that the definitions of the more obscure words are more specific, in interesting ways. And a third is—since I'm being honest here—that they sound cooler.

People have also commented that the faction names are different parts of speech—three nouns (Candor, Amity, Abnegation) and two adjectives (Dauntless, Erudite). (For the record, I love this kind of grammar consciousness.) I am aware of that, and it was something I thought about in revisions. The reason for the discrepancy is that each faction chose their own names independently, just as they wrote their own manifestos independently, and formed their own customs and rules independently (to a certain extent, anyway). Keeping that in mind, I tried to pick the words that made the most sense for each faction without considering the other factions too much.

Abnegation: 1. to refuse or deny oneself (some rights, conveniences, etc.); reject; renounce. 2. to relinquish; give up

VERONICA: *I like the verbs in that first definition: "refuse," "deny," "reject," "renounce"—active forms of stripping things from your life. As opposed to "relinquish," "give up" in the second definition—which are more passive.*

Amity: 1. friendship; peaceful harmony. 2. mutual understanding and a peaceful relationship, especially between nations; peace; accord. 3. cordiality

VERONICA: *It's not just about banjos and apple-picking. It's about cultivating strong relationships and trying to understand each other. Oh, Amity.*

Candor: 1. the state or quality of being frank, open, and sincere in speech or expression; candidness. 2. freedom from bias; fairness; impartiality.

VERONICA: *That definition helped me flesh out Candor more, particularly in the second book,* INSURGENT. *The faction is not just trying to develop honesty—they're also trying to develop impartiality.*

Dauntless: fearless, undaunted. (Undaunted: courageously resolute, especially in the face of danger or difficulty; not discouraged.)

VERONICA: *It's those two definitions ("fearless" and "undaunted") that I found so fascinating. Being fearless and being undaunted are two different things. And the characters in* DIVERGENT *struggle with that distinction.*

Erudite: characterized by great knowledge; learned or scholarly

VERONICA: *The word "erudite" focuses on knowledge rather than intelligence—intelligence being something you're born with and can't necessarily control, and knowledge being something that you acquire. I find that interesting, given what I know about Erudite.*

Character Naming
with Veronica Roth

Obviously I have a thing about names, or else Beatrice would not have become Tris, and Four would have gone by Tobias in the beginning. I believe the names we choose on our own can be powerful, and they can embody a new identity for us.

When I was young my mother wanted to call me Nikki (a less popular short form of Veronica) and I absolutely *refused* to respond to it. The same thing happened when people tried to call me Ronnie. I just wasn't having it. The nickname I chose was V. I think it's because it sounded less cutesy or girly. What I chose for myself was something that fit with my personality—I'm not exactly cutesy. (Though I am girlier now than I ever used to be—maybe that's why I don't go by V as much anymore?)

Name changing is also interesting from a religious perspective. In the Torah, when a biblical figure has an encounter with God, sometimes he or she is given a new name. Abram to Abraham, for example. Jacob to Israel. Sarai to Sarah. Same thing in the Bible—Saul becomes Paul; Simon becomes Peter. This usually signals the beginning of some kind of transformation or indicates that a transformation has already taken place.

If you want a more current example, think Mr. Anderson versus Neo in the Matrix movies, or Augustus versus Gus in *The Fault in Our Stars* (a little different, but interesting to consider, I think), or Andrew versus Ender in *Ender's Game*, or Tom Riddle versus Voldemort in the Harry Potter books and movies, or Anakin versus Darth Vader in Star Wars. (Wow, apparently I really *am* attracted to this concept, because it's in all the things I like. . . .)

It's like we have some kind of need, once we feel that we have changed, for people to call us something different. Is it for us, to suit the way we see ourselves? Or is it for them, to force them to think of us differently? Or a combination of both?

It's these musings about names that led to the Tobias/ Four divide in the first place. Four views Tobias as the name of a helpless little boy, so he chooses Four as the name of his adult self in an attempt to leave the pain behind him. It signifies his strength rather than his weakness. But what he finds is that he can't ignore his past; it keeps creeping up on him, especially in his fear landscape. So in DIVERGENT, he "gives" Tris his old identity—he trusts her to know his vulnerable side, the side of the child and not the man. She recognizes the significance of this, which is why she starts to call him Tobias. It's the name he gave to her, the one he trusted her with, and she begins to treasure it for that reason.

In INSURGENT, this name issue becomes a bit more complicated, but for Tris it's the same. Tobias is the name she chooses for him, because it represents his secret self, the one he showed her and her alone. She calls him Four when she's with other people, to help him keep his secrets, but in her head, he's always Tobias.

Now, I like the name Tobias (I seem to be in the minority, but that's okay!) but I, like most of you, do prefer the name Four, and honestly, I always intended for him to be called Four most of the time. So I tried really, really hard to make some kind of shift in Tris's mind so it would make sense for her to call him Four in INSURGENT. There are plenty of arguments for why she might do that, and I made all of them, I promise you. But what surprised me was that it never felt right; it didn't feel like what Tris would *really* do. So Tobias it is. She's very stubborn, you know. In INSURGENT, he's Tobias 95 percent of the time, because that's how Tris wanted it. You can feel free to keep calling him Four, though—I do!

Faction Quiz

1. You most want your friends and family to see you as someone who . . .

   a. Is willing to make sacrifices and help anyone in need.

   b. Is liked by everyone.

   c. Is trustworthy.

   d. Will protect them no matter what happens.

   e. Offers wise advice.

2. When you are faced with a difficult problem, you react by . . .

   a. Doing whatever will be the best thing for the greatest number of people.

   b. Creating a work of art that expresses your feelings about the situation.

   c. Debating the issue with your friends.

   d. Facing it head-on. What clsc would you do?

   e. Making a list of pros and cons, and then choosing the option that the evidence best supports.

3. What activity would you most likely find yourself doing on the weekend or on an unexpected day off?

   a. Volunteering

b. Painting, dancing, or writing poetry

c. Sharing opinions with your friends

d. Rock-climbing or skydiving!

e. Catching up on your homework or reading for pleasure

4. If you had to select one of the following options as a profession, which would you choose?

   a. Humanitarian

   b. Farmer

   c. Judge

   d. Firefighter

   e. Scientist

5. When choosing your outfit for the day, you select . . .

   a. Whatever will attract the least amount of attention.

   b. Something comfortable, but interesting to look at.

   c. Something that's simple, but still expresses your personality.

   d. Whatever will attract the most attention.

   e. Something that will not distract or inhibit you from what you have to do that day.

6. If you discovered that a friend's significant other was being unfaithful, you would . . .

a. Tell your friend because you feel that it would be unhealthy for him or her to continue in a relationship where such selfish behavior is present.

b. Sit them both down so that you can act as a mediator when they talk it over.

c. Tell your friend as soon as possible. You can't imagine keeping that knowledge a secret.

d. Confront the cheater! You might also take action by slashing the cheater's tires or egging his or her house—all in the name of protecting your friend, of course.

e. Keep it to yourself. Statistics prove that your friend will find out eventually.

7. What would you say is your highest priority in life right now?
   a. Serving those around you
   b. Finding peace and happiness for yourself
   c. Seeking truth in all things
   d. Developing your strength of character
   e. Success in work or school

Faction Quiz Results

If you chose mostly *A*s, you are **ABNEGATION**. You don't like to draw attention to yourself, and you are more concerned about other people's contentment than your own. You find joy and fulfillment in making other people happier, safer, and healthier. You believe that the world would be a better place if selfishness were not so widespread. Other people see you as somewhat difficult to get to know, but also as quiet and kind.

If you chose mostly *B*s, you are **AMITY**. You are at peace when the people around you are getting along. You appreciate music and the arts, and it is easy to make you laugh. One of your goals is to find as much happiness as you can. You believe that aggression and hostility are to blame for most of the world's problems. Others see you as sometimes flaky or indecisive, but also as easygoing and warm.

If you chose mostly *C*s, you are **CANDOR**. You are honest with everyone, no matter how difficult it is, and no matter how much trouble it gets you into. You aren't easily offended, and would prefer to hear the truth even if it hurts. You believe that if everyone could be honest and forthright with each other, the world would be a much better place. Other people see you as sometimes insensitive, but also as trustworthy and confident.

If you chose mostly *D*s, you are **DAUNTLESS**. You love a good adrenaline rush, and you don't let other people dictate your behavior. You do what you believe is right no matter how difficult or frightening it is. You believe that the world would be better off if people were not afraid to do what was necessary to make things right. Others see you as often abrasive, but also as strong and bold.

If you chose mostly *E*s, you are **ERUDITE**. You enjoy learning new things, and you try to understand how everything works. You tend to make decisions based on logic rather than instinct or emotions. You believe the world would be a better place if everyone were well-educated and devoted to learning. Other people see you as sometimes condescending, but also as intelligent and insightful.

Faction Manifestos

ABNEGATION: THE SELFLESS
FACTION MANIFESTO

I will be my undoing
If I become my obsession.

I will forget the ones I love
If I do not serve them.

I will war with others
If I refuse to see them.

Therefore I choose to turn away
From my reflection,
To rely not on myself
But on my brothers and sisters,
To project always outward
Until I disappear.*

(*Some members add a final line: "And only God remains." That
is at the discretion of each member, and is not compulsory.)

AMITY: THE PEACEFUL
FACTION MANIFESTO

Conversations of Peace

TRUST

A Son says to his Mother: "Mother, today I fought with my friend."

His Mother says: "Why did you fight with your friend?"

"Because he demanded something of me, and I would not give it to him."

"Why did you not give it to him?"

"Because it was mine."

"My son, you now have your possessions, but you do not have your friend. Which would you rather have?"

"My friend."

"Then give freely, trusting that you will also be given what you need."

SELF-SUFFICIENCY

A Daughter says to her Father: "Father, today I fought with my friend."

Her Father says: "Why did you fight with your friend?"

"Because she insulted me, and I was angry."

"Why were you angry?"

"Because she lied about me." (*In some versions: "Because I was hurt by her words."*)

"My daughter, did your friend's words change who you are?"

"No."

"Then do not be angry. The opinions of others cannot damage you."

FORGIVENESS

A Husband says to his Wife: "Wife, today I fought with my enemy."

His Wife says: "Why did you fight with your enemy?"

"Because I hate him."

"My husband, why do you hate him?"

"Because he wronged me."

"The wrong is past. You must let it rest where it lies."

KINDNESS

A Wife says to her Husband: "Husband, today I fought with my enemy."

Her Husband says: "Why did you fight with your enemy?"

"Because I spoke cruel words to her."

"My wife, why did you speak cruel words to her?"

"Because I believed them to be true."

"Then you must no longer think cruel thoughts. Cruel thoughts lead to cruel words, and hurt you as much as they hurt their target."

(The following section was part of the original manifesto, but was later removed.)

INVOLVEMENT

One Friend says to Another: "Friend, today I fought with my enemy."

The Other Friend says: "Why did you fight with your enemy?"

"Because they were about to hurt you."

"Friend, why did you defend me?"

"Because I love you."

"Then I am grateful."

CANDOR: THE HONEST
FACTION MANIFESTO

**DISHONESTY IS RAMPANT. DISHONESTY IS TEMPORARY.
DISHONESTY MAKES EVIL POSSIBLE.**

As it stands now, lies pervade society, families, and even the internal life of the individual. One group lies to another group, parents lie to children, children lie to parents, friends lie to friends, individuals lie to themselves. Dishonesty has become so integral to the way we relate to one another that we rarely find ourselves in authentic relationships with others. Our dark secrets remain our own. Yet it is our dark secrets that cause conflict. When we are dishonest with the people around us, we begin to hate ourselves for lying; when we are dishonest with ourselves, we can never even attempt to correct the flaws we find within us, the flaws we are so desperate to hide from our loved ones, the flaws that make us lie.

What has become clear is that lies are just a temporary solution to a permanent problem. Lying to spare a person's feelings, even when the truth would help them to improve, damages them in the long run. Lying to protect yourself lasts for so long before the truth emerges. Like a wild animal, the truth is too powerful to remain caged. These are examples we can clearly see in our own lives, yet we fail to understand that they do not just apply to the dynamic between ourselves and our neighbors, or ourselves and our friends.

What is society but a web of individual-to-individual relationships? And what is conflict except one person's dark secret crashing into another person's dark secret? Dishonesty is a veil that shields one person from another. Dishonesty allows evil to persist, hidden from the eyes of those who would fight it.

DISHONESTY LEADS TO SUSPICION. SUSPICION LEADS TO CONFLICT. HONESTY LEADS TO PEACE.

We have a vision of an honest world. In this world, parents do not lie to their children, and children do not lie to their parents; friends do not lie to one another; spouses do not lie to each other. When we are asked our opinions we are free to give them without having to consider any other responses. When we engage in conversation with others, we do not have to evaluate their intentions, because they are transparent. We have no suspicion, and no one suspects us.

And most of all—yes, above all else—we are free to expose our dark secrets because we know the dark secrets of our neighbors, our friends, our spouses, our children, our parents, and our enemies. We know that while we are flawed in a unique way, we are not unique because we are flawed. Therefore we can be authentic. We have no suspicions. And we are at peace with those around us.

TRUTH MAKES US TRANSPARENT. TRUTH MAKES US STRONG. TRUTH MAKES US INEXTRICABLE.

We will raise our children to tell the truth. We will do this by encouraging them to speak their minds at every moment. For the child, withholding words is the same as lying.

We will be honest with our children even at the expense of their feelings. The only reason people cannot bear honesty now is because they were not raised hearing the truth about themselves, and they can't stand to. If children are raised to hear both honest praise and honest criticism, they will not be so fragile as to crumble beneath the scrutiny of their peers. A life of truth makes us strong.

Adulthood will be defined as a time at which each member of society is capable of bearing every other member's dark secrets, just as every other member will bear theirs. Therefore each member will be subjected to The Full Unveiling, in which every hidden part of their life is laid bare before their fellow members. They, too, will see the hidden parts of their fellow members' lives. In this way we bear one another's secrets. In this way we become inextricable:

TRUTH

MAKES

US

INEXTRICABLE.

ERUDITE: THE INTELLIGENT
FACTION MANIFESTO

WE SUBMIT THE FOLLOWING STATEMENTS AS TRUTH:

1. "Ignorance" is defined not as stupidity but as lack of knowledge.
2. Lack of knowledge inevitably leads to lack of understanding.
3. Lack of understanding leads to a disconnect among people with differences.
4. Disconnection among people with differences leads to conflict.
5. Knowledge is the only logical solution to the problem of conflict.

Therefore, we propose that in order to eliminate conflict, we must eliminate the disconnect among those with differences by correcting the lack of understanding that arises from ignorance with knowledge. The areas in which people must be educated are:

SOCIOLOGY
- So that the individual understands how society at large functions.

PSYCHOLOGY

- So that the individual understands how a person functions within that society.

MATHEMATICS

- So that the individual is prepared for further study in science, engineering, medicine, and technology.

SCIENCE

- So that the individual better understands how the world operates.
- So that the individual's study in other areas is supplemented.
- So that as many individuals as possible are prepared to enter the fields devoted to innovation and progress.

COMMUNICATION

- So that the individual knows how to speak and write clearly and effectively.

HISTORY

- So that the individual understands the mistakes and successes that have led us to this point.
- So that the individual learns to emulate those successes and avoid those mistakes.

Leaders must not be chosen based on charisma, popularity, or ease of communication, all of which are misleading and have little to do with the efficacy of a political leader.

An objective standard must be used in order to determine who is best fit to lead. That standard will be an intelligence test, administered to all adults when the present leader reaches fifty-five or begins to decline in brain function in a demonstrable way.

Those who, after rigorous studying, do not meet a minimum intelligence requirement will be exiled from the faction so they can be made useful. This is not an act of elitism but rather one of practicality: Those who are not intelligent enough to engage in the roles assigned to us—roles that require a considerable mental capacity—are better suited to menial work than to faction work. Menial work is required for the survival of society, and is therefore just as important as faction work.

Information must always be made available to all faction members at all times. The withholding of information is punishable by reprimand, imprisonment, and, eventually, exile. Every question that can be answered must be answered or at least engaged. Illogical thought processes must be challenged when they arise. Wrong answers must be corrected. Correct answers must be affirmed. If an answer to a question is unclear, it must be put to debate. All debates require evidence. Any controversial thought or idea must be supplemented by evidence in order to reduce the potential for conflict.

Intelligence must be used for the benefit, and not to the detriment, of society. Those who use intelligence for their own personal gain or to the detriment of others have not properly borne the responsibility of their gift, and are not welcome in our faction.

It bears repeating: Intelligence is a gift, not a right. It must be wielded not as a weapon but as a tool for the betterment of others.

DAUNTLESS: THE BRAVE
FACTION MANIFESTO

WE BELIEVE

that cowardice is to blame for the world's injustices.

WE BELIEVE

that peace is hard-won, that sometimes it is necessary
to fight for peace. But more than that:

WE BELIEVE

that justice is more important than peace.

WE BELIEVE

in freedom from fear, in denying fear the power to
influence our decisions.

WE BELIEVE

in ordinary acts of bravery, in the courage that
drives one person to stand up for another.

WE BELIEVE

in acknowledging fear and the extent to which it rules us.

WE BELIEVE

in facing that fear no matter what the cost to our comfort,
our happiness, or even our sanity.

WE BELIEVE

in shouting for those who can only whisper, in
defending those who cannot defend themselves.

WE BELIEVE,
not just in bold words but in bold deeds to match them.
WE BELIEVE
that pain and death are better than cowardice
and inaction, because
WE BELIEVE
in action.

WE DO NOT BELIEVE
in living comfortable lives.
WE DO NOT BELIEVE
that silence is useful.
WE DO NOT BELIEVE
in good manners.
WE DO NOT BELIEVE
in limiting the fullness of life.
WE DO NOT BELIEVE
in empty heads, empty mouths, or empty hands.
WE DO NOT BELIEVE
that learning to master violence encourages
unnecessary violence.
WE DO NOT BELIEVE
that we should be allowed to stand idly by.
WE DO NOT BELIEVE
that any other virtue is more important than bravery.